# Ayurvedic Man

Encounters with Indian medicine

# Introduction

Medical knowledge and museum objects have long been contested sites of global encounters. In India, health narratives have shaped and been shaped by Tibetan, Persian, Greco-Islamic and European influences. Throughout such encounters they have morphed and expanded, acquiring new meanings, or have been misinterpreted and exoticised, changing old ones.

This book takes its title from the *Ayurvedic Man* – an 18th-century Nepali painting held at the Wellcome Library. It is a rare example of illustration in a South Asian medical manuscript, imbued with multiple cultural influences and inscribed by at least three makers – scholar, artist, calligrapher. Here, it becomes a springboard for shedding light on Wellcome's rich historical collections related to Ayurveda and Indian medicine.

Ayurveda, which roughly translates as 'knowledge of long life' (*veda* = knowledge + *āyus* = long life), is a centuries-old but ever-evolving set of South Asian medical practices that includes therapeutic massage, herbal medications and dietetics. At its core is a humoral conception of the medical body, in which disease relates to an imbalance of *vāta*, *pitta* and *kapha*, loosely translated as wind, bile and phlegm. Widely practised today in India and beyond, a more homogenised 'Modern Ayurveda' emerged in early 20th-century India as a response to the increasing authority of biomedicine during the British colonial administration. From the 1970s, a 'New Age' Ayurveda developed in the West as part of the wellness market.

The collections amassed by Henry Wellcome bear witness to the diverse transformations and cross-cultural exchanges of medical knowledge, practices and related cultural expressions. Following his ambition to "capture the art and science of healing through the ages", Wellcome amassed over a million artefacts through a worldwide network of collectors, auction houses and dealers. Many of the unique objects included in this book were collected by Dr Paira Mall in the Indian subcontinent between 1911 and 1917.

Mall was a physician born in India and trained in Europe, and also a linguist and expert on Asian cultures. His eclectic acquisitions ranged from Sanskrit medical manuscripts, Persian illustrated treatises and Tibetan anatomical maps to vibrant gouache paintings, erotic manuals and animal-shaped surgical tools. Instructed by the curator of Wellcome's museum – C J S Thompson – to also acquire local medical knowledge, Mall copied and translated ancient Ayurvedic manuscripts and purchased native medicinal plants used in local traditional medicine for the Wellcome Chemical Research Laboratories.

As plants, knowledge and museum objects get dispersed across the world, and while the healing narratives of Ayurveda continue to evolve, some questions remain: What is the contemporary relevance of traditional medical practices such as Ayurveda? How can museum collections reflect the myriad health conceptions, environmental attitudes and cosmologies that exist around the world? And more importantly, given the rising fascination with what has been labelled 'alternative medicine', what might authenticity mean in medical heritage, and who ultimately owns it?

**Bárbara Rodríguez Muñoz**
Curator, Wellcome Collection

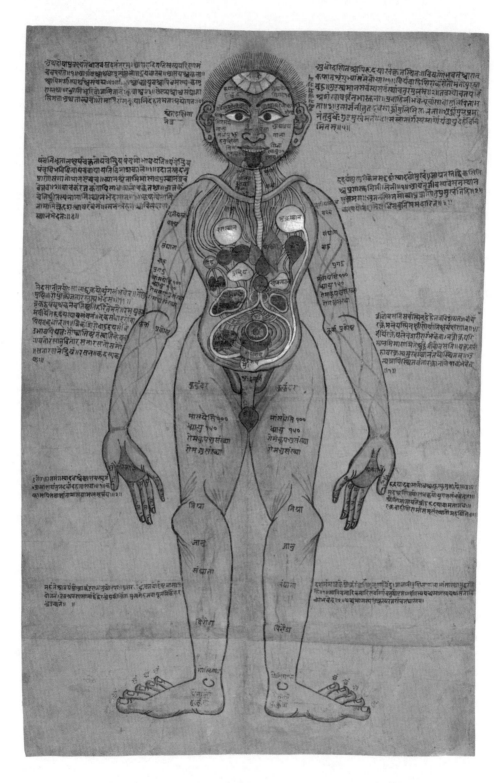

# Ayurvedic Man

Pen and watercolour, 18th century

*The heart is similar to a lotus, facing downwards. On waking up, it blooms; on sleeping, it closes up. That is the resting place of the soul. It is the supreme location of the consciousness. And so, when it is suffused with torpor, living creatures fall asleep.*

This unique 18th-century Nepali anatomical painting provides a visual interpretation of the organs and vessels of the male body according to classical Ayurveda. Its trail of provenance from Nepal via India to the Wellcome Library through an art dealer points to the long-standing European fascination with what is now often labelled as 'alternative medicine'.

As a knowledge system, Ayurveda is codified in a series of ancient Sanskrit medical texts and in modern manuals, but has also flowed more informally across diverse communities through domestic and eclectic beliefs, rituals and practices. Here, the *Ayurvedic Man* is surrounded by text from the third chapter of the 16th-century Sanskrit *Bhāvaprakāśa*, which focuses on anatomy and embryology:

"Now the humours will be described, and after that, the tissues... The body is thought to be made of these."

Scholars suggest that the painting resulted from a collaborative process between a physician, who was also a scholar of Ayurveda, one or more artists, possibly from Kathmandu, and a calligrapher who copied the texts but may not have been fluent in written Sanskrit, resulting in various errors and unintelligible terminology. As for the intended audience, reception and usage of the manuscript, these are questions that are open to speculation.

# Mapping
the Body

Alongside Ayurveda, traditional medical practices that have been revived in post-independence India include Unani (Greco-Arabic) and Siddha (Tamil). The physicians of each system, known respectively as *vaidyas*, *hakims* and *siddhars*, have practised and exchanged medical knowledge for centuries.

The traditional education system for each of these practices was modelled on the ancient *gurukula* system – that is, a teacher passing his knowledge down to several pupils through face-to-face interaction, from father to sons or uncle to nephews, often forming medical lineages. In the modern structure of Ayurvedic colleges, the standardised curricula and clinical training draw more heavily on biomedical terminology, techniques and therapies.

Today, the anatomical body within each traditional system has been reconciled with the dissected body of biomedical anatomy for diagnostic as well as therapeutic purposes. By contrast, earlier South Asian anatomical maps evoke a more expansive and poetic conception of the body as a fluent entity, charting emotions, blockages, *chakras* and metaphysical energies.

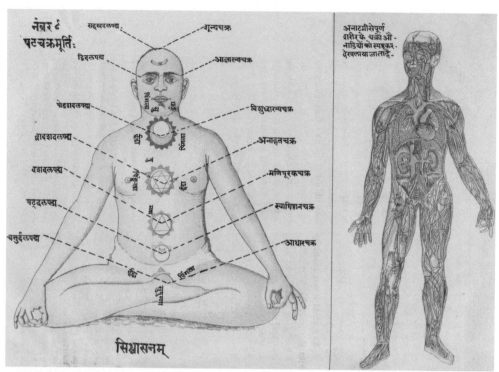

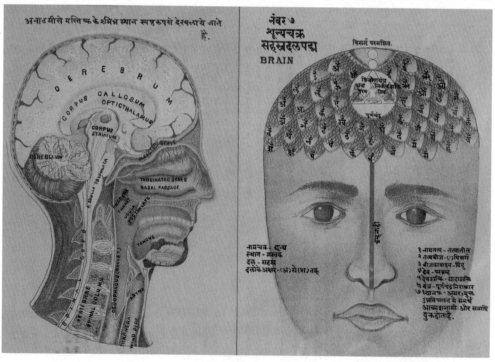

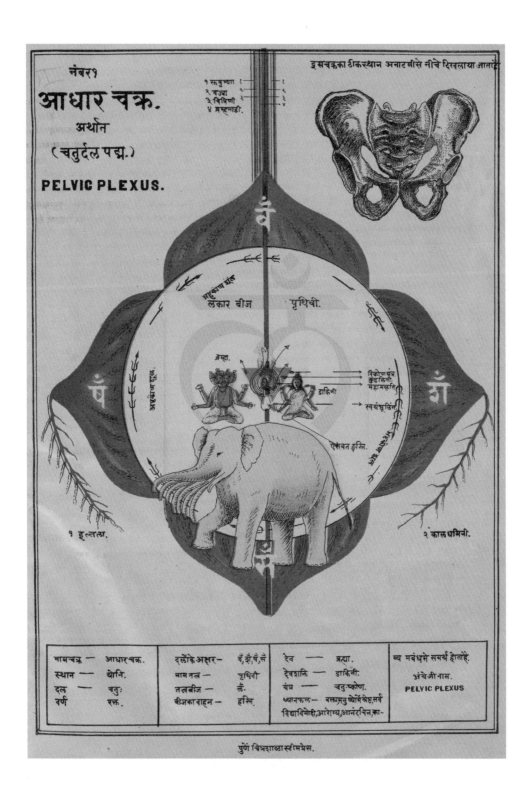

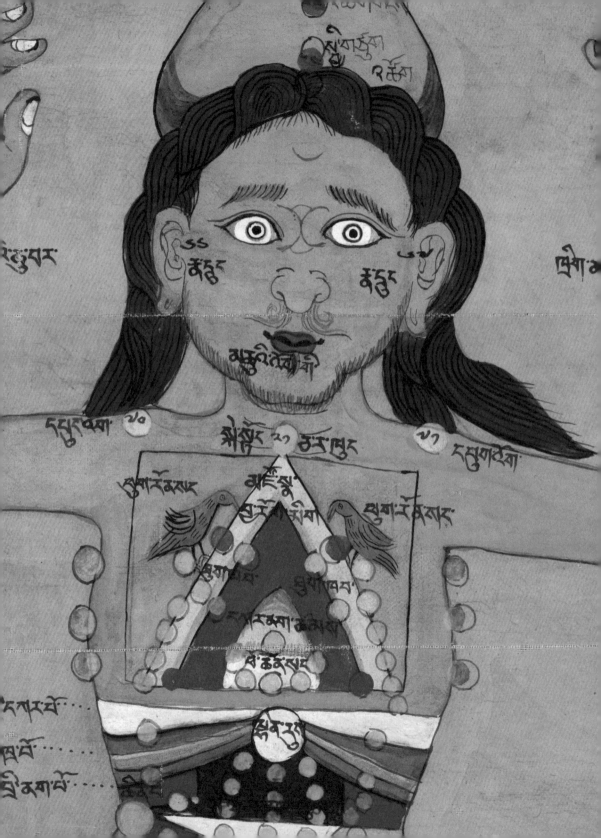

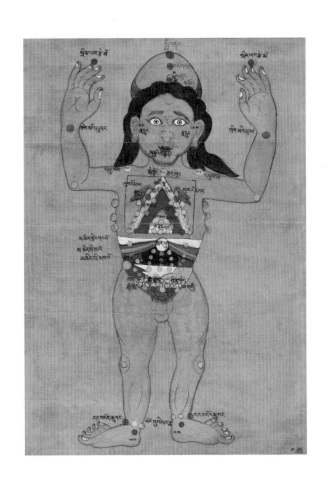

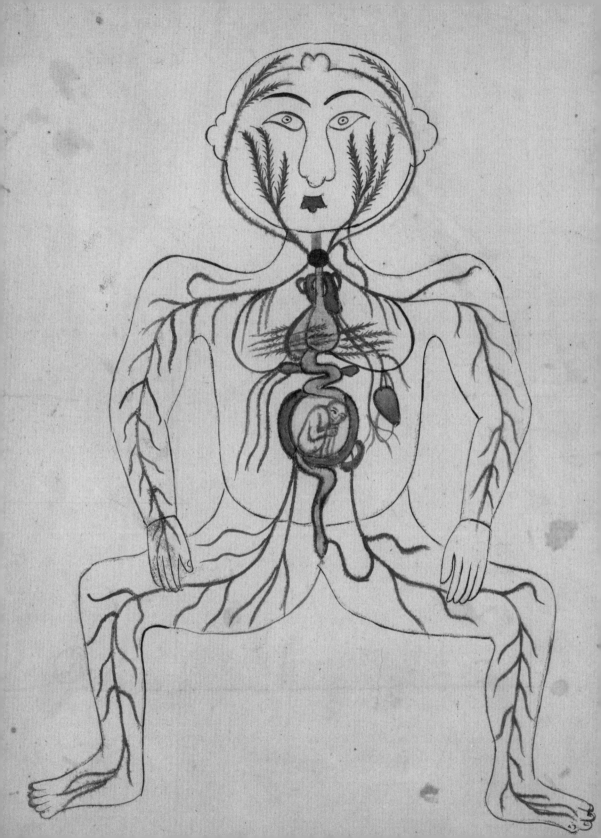

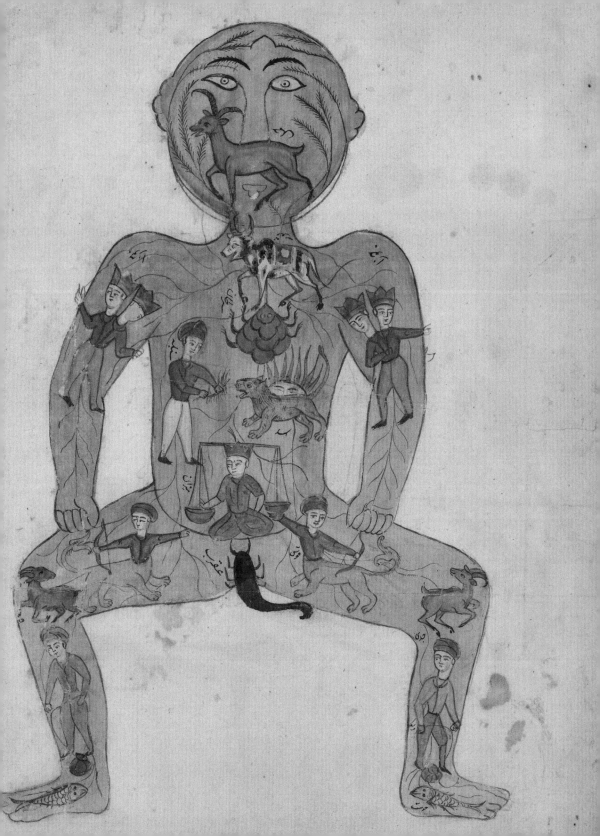

## Page 06

### A meditator shown with *chakras* and *kundalini*

Gouache on paper, 19th century

In the tantric view of the body, six *chakras* (points or vortexes of energy in the subtle body) are arranged along a vertical axis running from the base of the spinal column to the top of the head. A primal, coiled energy (*kundalini*), depicted as a serpent, may be raised to travel up the *chakras*, leading to spiritual awakening that manifests in the opening of the 'third eye', located in the general area of the pineal gland in the brain.

## Page 08—09

### *Svāmihaṃsasvarūpakṛtam Ṣaṭcakranirūpaṇacitram*

Drawings by Swami Haṃsasvarūpa, 1903

Colour plates taken from an illustrated textbook intended to educate a new generation of Ayurvedic practitioners in the context of the 19th-century revival of indigenous medicine in India. They juxtapose the yogic (or subtle) body and Western anatomy in order to suggest similarities between the systems. The top left image depicts different nerves and plexuses of the human body alongside a conceptual illustration of the locus of *prāṇāyāma*, breath control through yogic discipline.

## Page 10—11

### Bloodletting points and moxa points on the human body

Gouache painting, Tibet, 18th–19th century

Tibetan painting depicting bloodletting and moxa points on the body.

The moxa points shown refer to the practice of moxibustion, a popular therapy that features in traditional Tibetan medical systems. This involves burning the herb mugwort over acupuncture points on the body in order to stimulate the flow of blood and *qi* (the circulating life-force).

## Page 12

### Anatomical illustration showing the arteries of the body and a fetus in the womb

Diagram in the *Tashrīh-i Manṣūrī* style, watercolour, 19th century

In 1396 the Persian author Manṣūr ibn Ilyās composed a popular treatise on anatomy entitled *Tashrīh-i Manṣūrī*, a text on the five 'systems' of the body – bones, nerves, muscles, veins and arteries. It summarised many of the observations of the Greek physician Galen, and was the first such treatise to be accompanied by illustrations and drawings of the human body in anatomical detail.

## Page 13

### Illustration showing a Zodiac Man, with Persian annotations on the image

Diagram in the *Tashrīh-i Manṣūrī* style, watercolour, 19th century

Persian illustration relating the signs of the zodiac to human anatomy, suggesting that during certain months one would be ill-advised to medically treat the associated body part. Pisces (the fish, February–March) appears on the feet, Aries (the ram, March–April) is related to the head and Taurus (the bull, April–May) is shown on the neck.

## Page 14

### Indian anatomical painting

Black ink and watercolour in the *Tashrīh-i Manṣūrī* style on handmade oriental paper, 18th century

Painting presenting a primarily medical image emphasising the veins, arteries and intestinal tract. While the image of the body is similar to the style of the Persian *Tashrīh-i Manṣūrī* series, the text surrounding it is a mixture of Sanskrit and old Gujarati, which places its origins in western India.

It presents a view of the body that combines medical and tantric ideas. Alongside the anatomically accurate organs, the Indian artist added *chakras* to the spinal column and mythical and astrological animals below it.

# Botanicals

For centuries, the dissemination of plants, humans and crafts across continents has run in parallel with the exchange of botanical knowledge and its medical applications. Whether driven by an ambition to improve health or to follow commercial and entrepreneurial opportunities, people have traded plants and botanical substances, which have then been adopted and repurposed by new cultures.

From the early 16th century, European trading monopolies such as the Dutch or British East India Companies were active around the shores of India. They were driven across the oceans by the allure of the spice trade, searching for botanical gold in the form of pepper, cinnamon, cassia, nutmeg, turmeric and ginger. Instructed by the corporate or national entity they served, European botanists and physicians created taxonomies of Indian plants to fit Western schemes and mined indigenous pharmacopoeia to find treatments for Western maladies. At the same time, plant remedies from Europe and the New World, such as cinchona bark to treat malaria, were gradually introduced into South Asia.

Tênga. Latina.
ൻ ൬. Malabarica.
نارَجيل. Arabica.
माड़ी. Lingua Bramanica
antiqua.

18

Fig. 1.

Antoni Jacobi Goedkint delineavit.    B. Stoopendael fecit.

19

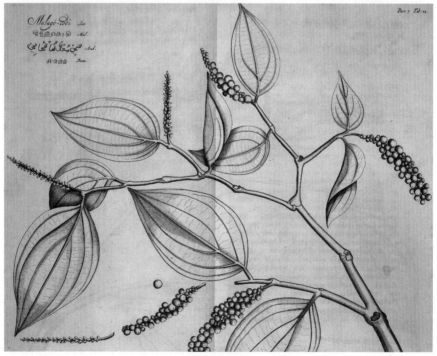

20

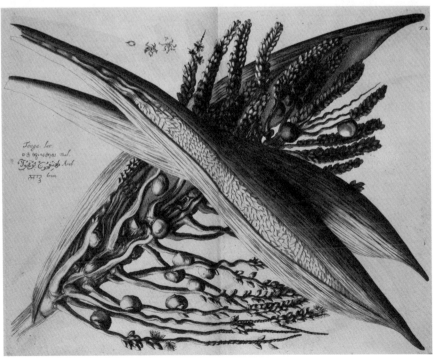

21

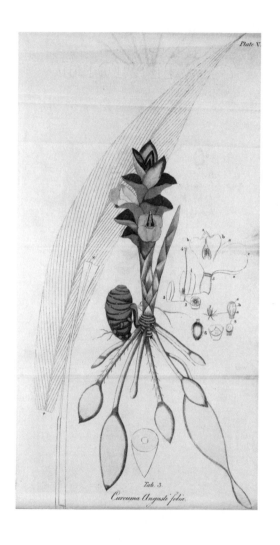

Tab. 3.

*Curcuma Angusti folia.*

Tab. 4

*Amomum Aculeatum.*

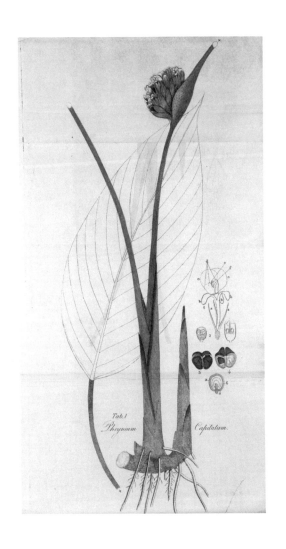

Tab.1
*Phrynium*      *Capitatum.*

Tab.4
*Zingiber Cassumunar.*

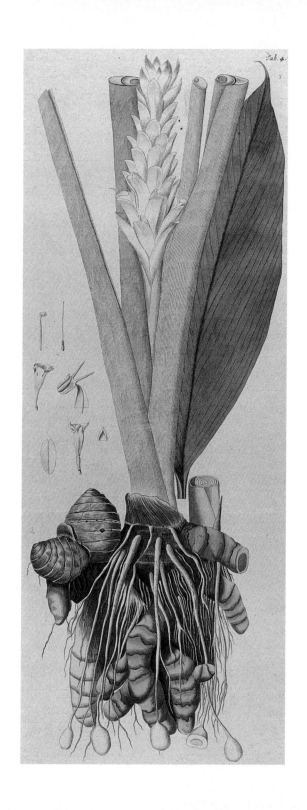

## Page 16

### Hanuman bringing the mountain to the injured Lakshmana

Watercolour, 19th century

In the South Asian epic the *Rāmāyana*, Lakshmana, the god Rāma's younger brother, was fatally wounded, and the only cure was *sanjeevani*, a magical herb that grew on a Himalayan mountain. When Hanuman – the monkey god, patron also of wrestling gymnasia – arrived at the Medicine Mountain, he could not identify the herb, and so carried back the entire mountain.

## Page 18—21

### *Hortus Indicus Malabaricus*

Hendrik Adriaan van Rheede, 1683–1703

Illustrations taken from an exquisitely illustrated 12-volume botanical text that provides a detailed account of the medicinal properties of 742 plants from Malabar (present-day Kerala in southern India). It was the result of a unique collaboration between Hendrik Adriaan van Rheede – the governor of Dutch Malabar – and local Brahmin scholars, lower-caste Ayurvedic physicians and plant gatherers, who provided the indigenous medico-botanical knowledge.

The text continues to be relevant to botanists and environmentalists today.

## Page 22—23

### *Catalogue of Indian Medicinal Plants and Drugs, with Their Names in the Hindustani and Sanskrit Languages*

John Fleming, 1812

Taken from a 19th-century catalogue detailing the medicinal properties of Indian plants, these illustrations were intended for use by medical professionals arriving in India from overseas. The plants featured in the catalogue are named in English, Hindustani and Sanskrit so that they could be more easily obtained.
(L—R: *Curcuma angustifolia*, *Amomum aculeatum*, *Phrynium capitatum*, *Zingiber cassumunar*)

## Page 24—25

### A drying room in the opium factory at Patna, India

After W S Sherwill, lithograph, c.1850

The British East India Company established a monopoly on opium cultivation in the Indian provinces of Bengal and Bihar – where the Company developed a method of growing opium poppies cheaply and abundantly – and manufacturing opium in the form of tablets, cakes and pellets that were prescribed as painkillers.

## Page 26—27

### Ascetics preparing opium outside a rural dwelling in India

Gouache painting, c.1810

In South Asian pharmacopeia, opium was considered not a poison but a therapeutic substance with a range of narcotic and medicinal properties. Unknown to early Ayurveda, it is said to have been introduced through contact with Islamic medical practices in the medieval era. While most notorious for its narcotic use, it was also prescribed by Western and indigenous medical practitioners to treat malarial fever, cholera and diarrhoea.

## Page 28

### Turmeric: rhizome with flowering stem and separate leaf and floral segments

Coloured engraving after F von Scheidl, 1776

*Curcuma longa* (turmeric) has been used for generations in India to heal wounds and burns. In 1999 the Indian government won a legal case to withdraw a US patent that had been filed for turmeric root's medicinal use. India's successful counterclaim argued that traditional medicinal knowledge could not be subjected to intellectual appropriation – an event that highlights the paradoxes and complexities around ownership of medical heritage.

# Surgery and Therapeutics

*Pañcakarma* (*pañca* = five + *karma* = actions) is a five-fold Ayurvedic purification and detoxification regime that involves a combination of massage using therapeutic oils, herbal therapy, and purgative or emetic procedures. Designed to eliminate harmful *doshas* (humours) from the body, the five procedures in the treatment's classical form are *vasti* (enema), *vamana* (emesis), *virechana* (purgation), *nasya* (nasal medicine) and *raktamoksha* (bloodletting).

With the revival of Ayurveda in India in the 19th and 20th centuries came a process of systematisation, standardisation and sanitisation. Modern Ayurveda reasserted the authenticity of classical codified knowledge, overlooking centuries of regional variations, folk rituals and other traditions.

Scholars and cosmopolitan practitioners today associate classical Ayurveda with three foundational Sanskrit texts compiled before the fifth century: the *Caraka Saṃhitā*, the *Suśruta Saṃhitā* and *Aṣṭāṅgahṛdaya Saṃhitā*. While many Ayurvedic scholars suggest that these texts are grounded in empiricism, others argue that they have divine and mythical origins, encapsulating the wisdom of ancient sages.

Beginning in the 1960s and 1970s, a New Age approach to Ayurveda emerged in Europe and the USA that favoured pharmaceutical and dietary over-the-counter products, self-help literature, and lifestyle preventive approaches to achieve 'wellness'. *Pañcakarma* gradually changed to privilege holistic massage over other remedies, eventually phasing out emetic or purgative procedures that did not fit stereotypes of New Age wellness.

كولنگ

حجام

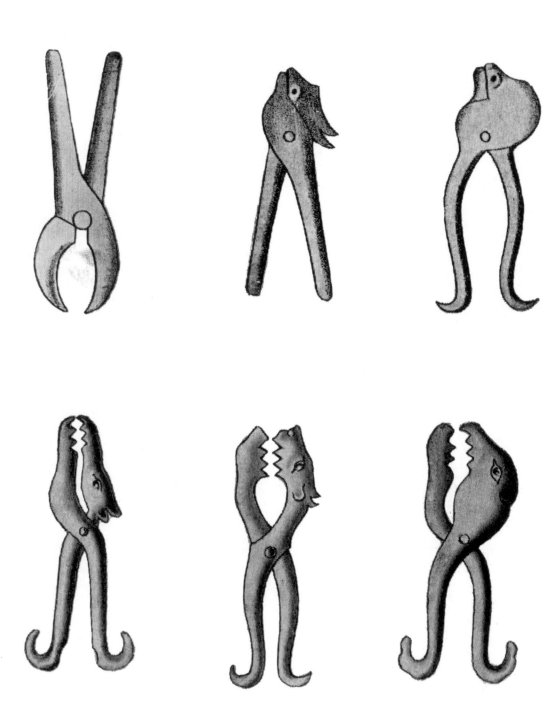

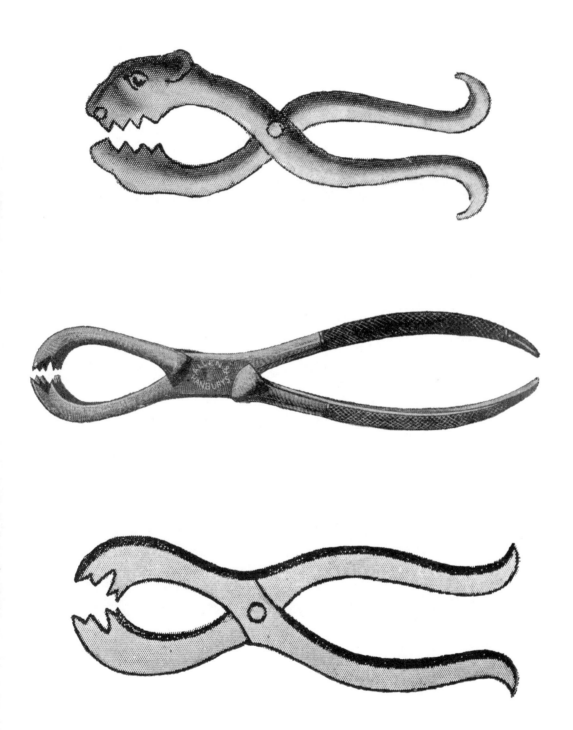

41

## Page 30, 32—33

### Company School paintings commissioned by Colonel James Skinner

Gouache paintings with pencil, 1825

'Company School painting' is a broad term for a variety of hybrid painting styles that developed in 18th- and 19th-century India as a result of European (especially British) East India Company patronage of Indian artists. The paintings served to document everyday scenes from Indian life, illustrating the various castes and occupations as well as the architecture and wildlife of the subcontinent.

The images depict a variety of surgical and therapeutic practices – including visits to Ayurvedic vaidyas and Unani hakims – some of which are now considered 'subaltern' healing techniques aimed at everyday health maintenance.

The paintings show: an eye surgeon operating on a man; (L–R) an astrologer of the Brahmin caste outside his dwelling; a barber attending to a man's hair; an Ayurvedic medical practitioner taking the pulse; an ear cleaner at work.

## Page 34—35

### The Surgical Instruments of the Hindus

Girindranāth Mukhopādhyāya, 1913–14

Attributed to the Indian physician Suśruta, the *Suśruta Saṃhitā*, compiled somewhere between the third and fourth centuries CE, is renowned for its detailed exposition on surgery.

It describes sharp and blunt surgical tools resembling familiar animals and birds, which are depicted in this later 20th-century text. These cruciform instruments are shaped like the swastika, one of the signs of the Jinas (spiritual victors in Jainism), with arms crossing each other. Suśruta explains how each shape had a specific purpose: "If the foreign body is visible, extract it by the lion forceps. If it is invisible, it should be extracted by the heron forceps."

Replicas were produced in India during British colonial rule, at a time when there was a revival of interest in Indian surgery among European medics.

## Page 36—37

### Sri Lankan ivory enema syringe

1751–1800

An enema syringe collected by King Keerthi Sri Rajasinghe, a popular monarch who ruled what is now Sri Lanka between 1747 and 1782 and was close to the British rulers.

The herbal enema (or *vasti*) is one of the five *pañcakarma* treatments used in Ayurveda to detoxify and restore balance to the body.

## Page 38—39

### Tibetan protection painting

Watercolour on paper, 19th century

Chart indicating good and bad bloodletting days and when to guard against demons.

Bloodletting (or *raktamoksha*), another of the five therapies of *pañcakarma*, is used to remove excess *pitta dosha* from the bloodstream and restore the body to balance and health. In Ayurveda, a *pitta* imbalance is believed to cause skin conditions such as eczema or skin discolouration, as well as inflammation.

## Page 40—41

### A pair of wrestlers and an Indian wrestler seated

Indian album of illustrations, 19th century

Wrestling takes place in *akharas* (gymnasia), but extends to an elaborate way of life involving general prescriptions of physical culture, diet, health, ethics and morality.

*Akharas* function like health retreats, creating a therapeutic environment where many go to treat minor ailments such as constipation, arthritis, backaches, skin infections, bruises and sprains.

Page 42—43

## An Indian person in a yogic posture

Gouache painting, 19th century

Yoga emerged in India as a method to transcend suffering and seek enlightenment. In parallel with Ayurveda's own transformations, by the late 19th century printed images of yogic bodies (which mapped metaphysical energies) reflected a slow but visible transformation as a result of encounters with the world of science.

In contemporary global spa culture and yoga studios, yoga has moved from an avenue for spiritual transformation to a means of achieving physical wellbeing.

# Gender
# and Sexuality

In most early medical texts – whether Indian, Tibetan, Chinese or Greco-Arabic – the male medical voice and gaze is predominant, while reports on the female lived experience are rare. This is similarly the case for issues of sex, gender, women's health or diseases of the reproductive system. Illustrations of anatomical features or medical conditions are usually depicted using male figures, unless the text specifically discusses a gendered condition that only affects women. Not surprisingly, even early erotic manuals were primarily directed at the male ruling classes.

Family planning and birth control are complex and multi-layered issues, and debates and reforms involving these matters had a direct impact on maternal and infant health. Meanwhile, domestic medicine – natural or botanical remedies that were administered mainly by women from their homes or kitchens – has remained popular, despite the gradual influx of commercial and mass-produced Ayurvedic medications.

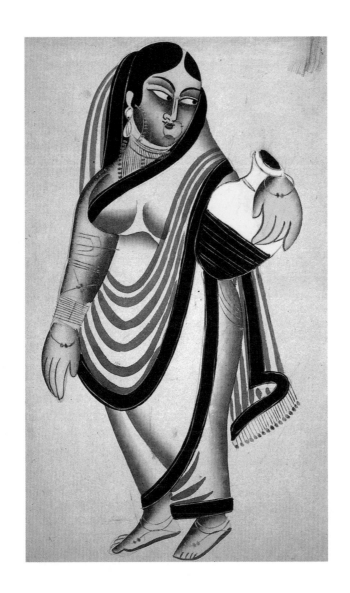

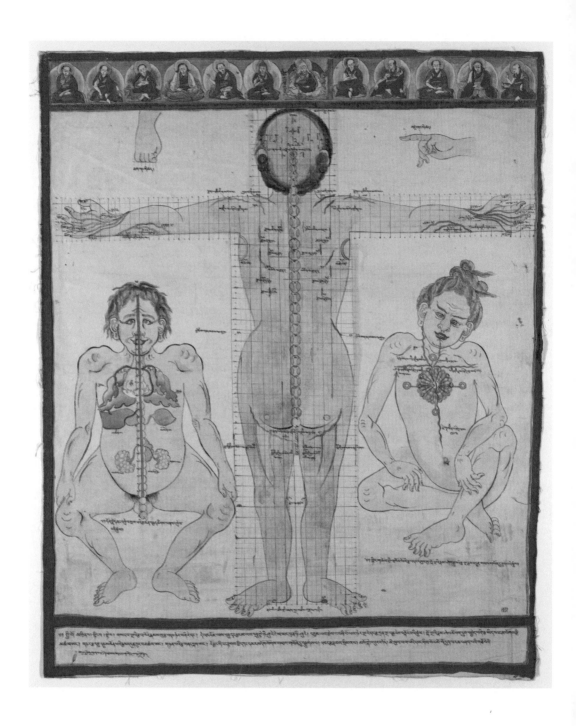

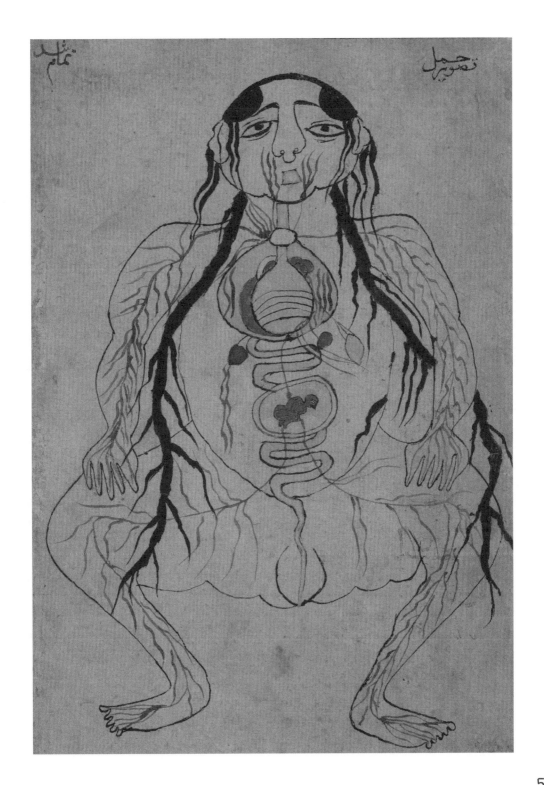

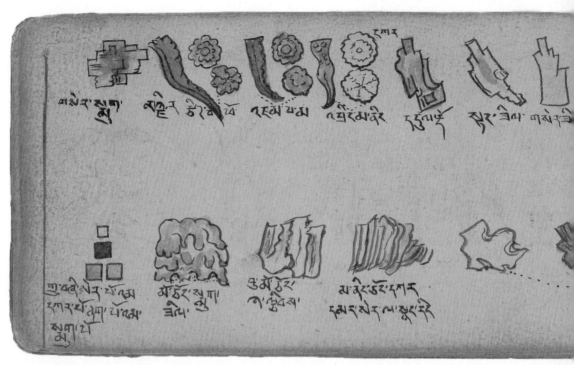

བ་མེར་སྐུག། བ་ཕྱིར་རྗེར་ཞ་ལོ། འདམ་ལོ་པ་མ། འབུ་རྡོག་མ་ནེར། དུ་ག་རྗེ། སྦུར་ཞིག་གཟེར་རེ།

ལྭ་འཕྱེ་མེར་ཡོ་ཕྱ། དག་ར་ཕོ་ལྕུག་ཕོ་འཕྱ། སྐུག་ཕོ། མ་ཕྱུར་སྐུག་ཞེ་ས། ཅ་མོ་ཕྱེར་ཞ་ལྕུ་ཞ། མ་ནེར་ཕྱོ་དུག་ར། དམ་ར་མེར་ལ་སྒུར་རེ།

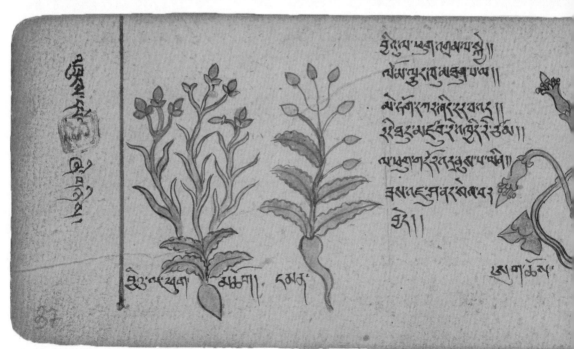

འབྲུས་པར་ཞེ་འདའ་པ།

ཉེའུ་ལ་ཕྲ་འཕགས་ཡ་སྐྱི། ཡོམ་ལྕུར་ཕ་ཕ་རྒྱུ་ཡ། ཡེ་ཞོག་ལྟ་རྗེ་ར་ཕད། ར་ཞ་ར་མ་རྗོ་ཕ་རྗེ་རྐྱ། ལ་རྒུག་རྗེ་ར་དྲུས་པ་ཞེ། ཐམས་ཇ་རྗ་ཕ་ར་ལོ་ཕ་ར། ཞེ།

ཕྱེ་ས་ཡ་སྦུལ། མ་ཚ་གa། དཔལ། ཞ་ག་ཆེས།

ཤུག་ལ་མ།   ཆབ་རག་ར   བཛྲ་པ་ཨ་རྐྱིཥ

མོ་ཚེ

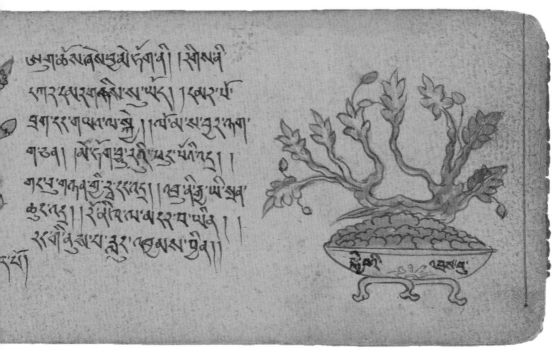

ཨ་ག་ཚ་བ་ནས་ཤུ་ཡེ་ཏ་ག་ཡི། སེཥ་ནེ
དང་ར་མར་ར་ཀླེ་ཤ་ཡོད། ཁར་ར་བོ
ཐག་ར་ག་ཡབ་ལ་ཟུ། བོ་ཤ་ཤ་ནུར་ཏ་བ།
ག་ནུ། མེ་ཏོ་བ་བུ་རུ། ཤུར་ཡོ་ཏ།
ག་ར་ག་ནས་ནུ་ཙ་ར་རང་། ཟ་ཨེ་ཙུ་ཡེ་ཤ།
རུ་ར་ཏུ། རེ་ཡི་ཁ་མར་ར་བ་ཡོ།
རེ་ལོ་རུ་མ་ཟ་རུ་ཚུ་འཆམས་ཆེ།
ཨ་ཡོ།

ཥི་ལི   འབར་ཏུ

### Page 46

**Two lovers surrounded by an oval frame**

Watercolour drawing, West Bengal, 19th century

### Page 48

**Woman swinging below an aubergine plant**

Watercolour with pencil, 19th century

Watercolour done in a traditional 19th-century style known as Kalighat painting. Kalighat style covered subjects ranging from religious imagery of Hindu gods and goddesses to natural history and ethnographic scenes of daily life.

As an indigenous remedy, the aubergine, or brinjal (*Solanum melongena*), is used to treat conditions such as inflammation, neuralgia, cardiac debility, ulcers, bronchitis, cholera, asthma, fever and general weakness.

### Page 49

**Woman with a pitcher**

Watercolour drawing, 19th century

### Page 50

**Three Tibetan anatomical figures**

Watercolour on linen, early 19th century

A copy of one of a set of 80 paintings commissioned by Sangye Gyamtso (regent of the Fifth Dalai Lama) as part of his treatise *The Blue Beryl*, a commentary on the *Four Tantras* – the basic text of Tibetan medicine. The figures illustrate anatomical features, largely focusing on certain blood vessels as well as channels in the body connected with the states of consciousness and emotion.

Male figures seem to be the norm in anatomical illustration, and the figure on the left depicts a male organ at the end of the spine. However, none of the male anatomical parts – penis, scrotum – are identifiable or labelled, nor are they mentioned in the relevant sections of *The Blue Beryl*.

### Page 51

**The body of a pregnant woman with a fetus in a breech position, depicted with lettering in Persian**

Watercolour, 19th century

One of a series of six, the diagram is in the style of the anatomical illustrations found in the *Tashrīh-i Manṣūrī*.

The last chapter of Manṣūr's manuscript mentions complex organs and the development of embryos. Although there are similarities between Manṣūr's illustrations and earlier Persian anatomical drawings, a colour illustration of the uterus during pregnancy – in a similar style to that shown – is thought by some scholars to be one of the first illustrations of its kind.

### Page 52

*Caraka Saṃhitā, the Compendium of Caraka*

1393 manuscript (original treatise authored between 350 BCE and 450 CE)

The *Caraka Saṃhitā* – alongside the *Aṣṭāṅgahṛdaya Saṃhitā* (Heart of the Eight Parts) and the *Suśruta Saṃhitā* – is regarded as one of the three foundational texts of classical Indian medicine. The chapter displayed elaborates on breast feeding and provides remedies to be used when breast milk is of "abnormal taste", "excessively frothy", "rough", of "abnormal colour", with "foul odour", or is "unctuous", "slimy" or "heavy".

## Page 53

### *Ananga Ranga*, illustrated erotic manuscript

18th-century copy of a 15th- or 16th-century manuscript

Leaf from a copy of the *Ananga Ranga* (Stage of Love) manuscript, a 15th-century Indian sex manual that is often compared with the *Kama Sutra*.

From the 17th century onwards, erotic subjects were popular with kings and aristocrats in Nepal. As a result, the text is in both Sanskrit and Newari (which was then the administrative language of Nepal). The Sanskrit is written above and below the miniatures, with vernacular commentary in Newari written in the outer borders.

## Page 54—55

### *Illustrated Medical Simples of the Four Tantras*, Tibeto-Mongolian manuscript

Ink and watercolour on paper, 19th century

Tibetan medicine both absorbed and responded to early medical works from the Indian, Greco-Arabic, Chinese and indigenous Himalayan traditions. There are passages in the *Four Tantras* related to women's medicine that closely reproduce those found in Ayurvedic medical texts. One of the eight branches of medicine in the *Four Tantras* is dedicated to illnesses specific to women.

By contrast, women's diseases in Ayurvedic texts did not constitute a separate section, and were grouped in with information about treatments for reproductive illnesses, pregnancy, childbirth and childcare.

# Sickness
# and Spirituality

Ayurveda draws upon a set of Indian intellectual traditions – among them Nyaya, Vaisesika, Jyotisa, Samkhya and Buddhism – to conceive the healthy body as an entity in dynamic equilibrium with environmental, social and cosmological forces.

Traditional Indian science was interlinked with cosmology and astrology, which meant that there was room for otherworldly conceptions of health and disease beyond the material realm. Across India, there are multiple gods and goddesses identified with specific diseases – a phenomenon that was described in derogatory terms by colonialists as there being myriad vernacular "godlings of disease" in popular beliefs.

One of the eight limbs or branches (*ashta ānga*) of Ayurveda – alongside those focusing on surgery, sex, treatments for disease, ageing, poisons, the eyes, and (collectively) the ears, nose and throat – is referred to as Bhuta Vidya (Spirit Knowledge). Bhuta Vidya deals with diseases of unknown origin presumably deriving from supernatural causes – a broad category that coheres with bacterial or viral infection on the one hand as well as mental illness on the other.

In an attempt to modernise Ayurveda as a rational system of medicine, free from religious dogma or superstition, throughout the 20th century it was gradually stripped of its mystical elements, thereby marginalising its healing mantras and distancing it from supernatural causes of illness.

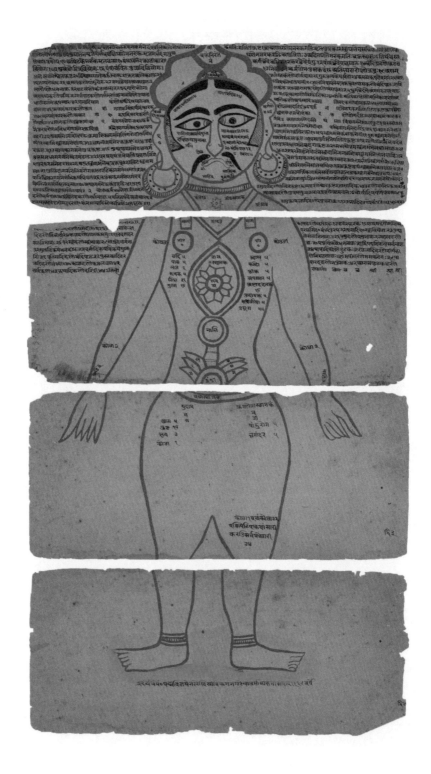

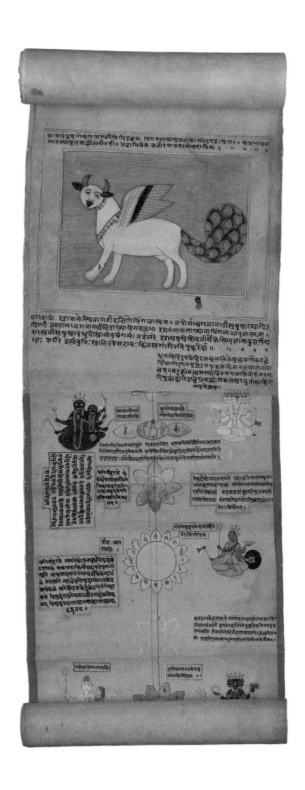

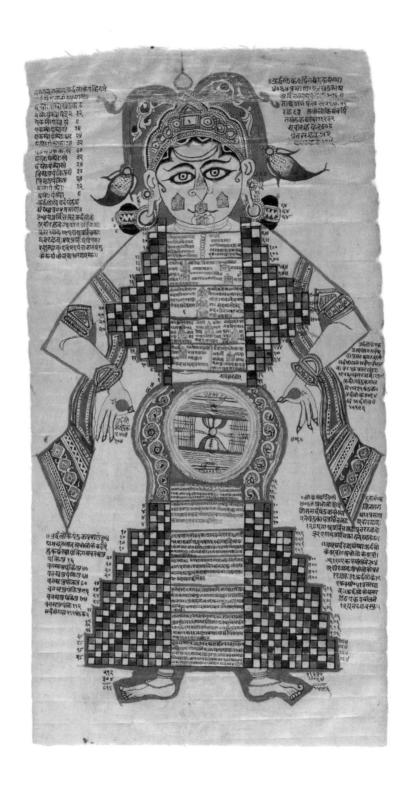

64

## Page 58

**Kali and all her symbols**

Watercolour drawing, West Bengal, 19th century

Kali is an incarnation of Durga, the Hindu goddess of epidemics and disease.

## Page 60—61

**Shiva and Parvati in a procession led by Brahma, Hanuman and attendants**

Gouache drawing, 19th century

A procession of Hindu gods, demigods and their attendants parading through the countryside. Shiva (the destroyer of evil) and Parvati (goddess of fertility and love) are depicted at the centre riding their favoured animal mount, the sacred bull Nandi.

## Page 62

**Sanskrit manuscript from the *karma vipāka* genre, meaning 'the ripening of karma'**

1469

Sanskrit manuscript beginning with a salutation to the Hindu sage Dhanvantari, physician of the gods and god of Ayurveda. It explains the karmic relationship with a given disaster or disease. For example, killing a cow will cause the killer to go to hell, while having sex with a priest's wife, the wife of another, a widow or a prostitute may lead to diseases such as ring-leprosy and symptoms such as bloody bile or excessive urination.

## Page 63

**Illustrated tantric scroll**

18th century

Scroll showing the rewards that devotees receive from worshipping and obeying demigods. At the top is a mythical creature displaying the features of various animals, including the tail of a peacock and the bill of a crow. Below, to the left, are Mahakala and Mahakali, god and goddess of fire, to the right is a Hakini – or demigod – with seven faces.

## Page 64

**Jain textile**

Watercolour on textile, Indian subcontinent, 16th century

Textile depicting the Jain concept of the universe in the form of a cosmic man.

Jainism is an ancient religion that originated in the Indian subcontinent in the sixth century BCE. According to Jain principles, living beings reincarnate over vast periods of time within four cycles of life – the infernal, animal, divine and human. Eventually, by developing spiritual knowledge and (re)gaining the correct understanding of the cosmos, the soul – released from its mortal remains – becomes perfected.

## Page 65

**Illustrated manuscript depicting Jain cosmology**

Ink and watercolour on paper, date unknown

In the manuscript, the circular disk represents the Madhya-loka (middle-world) and contains Mount Meru, which is surrounded by seas and continents inhabited by humans and animals. Above the central axis are the Urdhva-loka (heavenly worlds), where celestial beings reside. The Adho-loka (lower worlds) or hell-like realms are below and detail infernal scenes. Surrounding the *loka* (world) is the *aloka* (non-world).

## Page 66

**The Hindu creation story**

Olfert Dapper, engraving, 1672

A depiction of the original creation myth in Hinduism, the image shows the churning of the Ocean of Milk by gods and demons, using the serpent Vasuki as a rope. Supporting the churning at the bottom of the ocean are Kurma the turtle (the second incarnation of Vishnu), some mythical beasts and the kneeling Dhanvantari, who delivers Amrit, the nectar that grants immortality.

# Colonialism
# and Collecting

British colonial rule in India, from Company regimes to Crown administrations, lasted for over two centuries. Indian encounters with Western medicine during this period outline tensions between Indian and Western medical knowledge, between modernity and tradition, and between empire and colony.

Before 1800, Western biomedicine in India was largely confined to European enclaves and ports; the various forms of indigenous medical practice remained largely unaffected by colonial contact. Europeans sometimes consulted Indian *hakims* and *vaidyas*, believing that local doctors would be more familiar with local diseases, ecologies and climates. But once the East India Company monopolies gave way to British Crown rule, this more tolerant 'Orientalist' phase was quickly followed by a period of Anglicist suspicion and hostility toward indigenous medicine, which was seen as riddled with superstition and quackery.

By the end of the 19th century, Western biomedicine had acquired a significant degree of authority across British India, claiming superior efficacy as well as universal applicability. New biomedical hospitals, modelled on Western examples, spread across the country, while indigenous systems re-emerged in different forms by way of response and reaction.

70

*A Dramatic representation of the pon*

*From an Origin*

London Published by Longman

*Hindoo Goddess of the Small Pix.*

Drawing.

see page 33.

*rown. April 1, 1815.*

## Page 68

One man in traditional religious clothing (identified as Maharaja Ranjit Singh, the founder of the Sikh Empire), the other in European dress

Watercolour, c.1880

## Page 70—71

*The Holy Cow World Mother*

Raja Ravi Varma, chromolithograph, late 19th/early 20th century

Poster by artist Raja Ravi Varma from Kerala, whose pioneering paintings and lithographs were the first to unite European realist painting styles with Hindu mythology. It depicts the cow as a symbol of India in full health, abundant with milk, which is revered as one of the purest foods in Ayurvedic texts and thought to nourish all tissues in the body. The Holy Cow's body is divided up between many holy men, deities and natural elements, while the King of Justice prays and a farmer gives milk to Indian Hindus, Parsees and colonial Englishmen alike. The text is in Devanāgarī script, an alphabet developed in India and Nepal.

## Page 72—73

'Sitala, Hindu Goddess of the Small-pox', frontispiece in *The History of the Small Pox*

James Moore, watercolour on paper, 1815

Smallpox treatment revealed a clash between health belief systems. In the South Asian context, smallpox was understood not as a disease but as a divine presence, embodied by the goddess Sitala, who was widely worshipped across India.

Before the early 19th century, the medical practice of variolation – inoculation with live smallpox matter to produce a moderated form of the disease, and therefore protection against it – was widespread. Variolation had coexisted with Hindu beliefs acknowledging Sitala's rights over the patient's body, so smallpox was treated with a combination of medical intervention and religious worship. Vaccination, on the other hand, was introduced by the British administration in the early 19th century and was immediately seen as a colonial, secular and alien practice, at risk of incurring the wrath of Sitala and representing the unwelcome authority of external power over the individual and community.

## Page 74

Flushing engine cleansing infected houses, Bombay plague photograph album

Captain C Moss, 1896–97

The Bombay Plague Committee enforced rigorous measures to contain Bombay's first plague epidemic in 1896. Methods such as inspection, disinfection, segregation and hospitalisation, which ignored traditional Indian taboos of caste, community and gender, triggered vigorous opposition from native populations.

From 1900, the more intrusive anti-plague measures designed to gain control over the outbreaks – mainly in the form of segregation and sanitation – were abandoned as a consequence of Indian opposition. It became apparent that British medical intervention could only be effective if it was sensitive to local cultural and caste affinities and if it worked closely with local leaders.

From the late 1940s, a series of government reports addressed the issue of indigenous medicine to give it a more prominent role in public health measures against infectious diseases.

# Drawing
# the Bombay Plague

**Ranjit Kandalgaonkar, drawing and digital work, 2017**

The Bombay plague of 1896 marked a turning point in disease control. Strict, authoritarian measures were imposed by a colonial administration worried that the plague would spread back to Europe via its trade routes.

This new art commission combines imagery from two collections: photographs and documents from Wellcome's collection that chronicle the often draconian measures of the authorities, and satirical cartoons from the 1896 Bombay magazine *Pickings from the Hindi Punch*, held at the Asiatic Library in Mumbai, that veer between lampooning officials and illustrating common myths regarding the plague.

The map to the left depicts the plague as it began to grip the city of Bombay. It shows an area called Mandvi, where the first case of the disease was identified before spreading rapidly. Nearby are the Victoria dock and Prince's dock, where the rats and fleas from ships were suspected to be the original means of the disease spreading, though this was contested at the time.

Text by Ranjit Kandalgaonkar.
Ranjit Kandalgaonkar's commission follows from his residency at Gasworks, London, which was supported by the Charles Wallace India Trust and Inlaks Shivdasani Foundation.

# About the Collector

# Paira Mall

In 1911, Paira Mall, a doctor and linguist born in India and trained in Europe – was sent to India to source material for Henry Wellcome's Historical Medical Museum in London. Instructed to collect a wide and diverse range of objects, he was also encouraged to acquire local medical knowledge by copying and translating ancient manuscripts and purchasing native medicinal plants for the Wellcome Chemical Research Laboratories.

Mall was a well-travelled doctor who had served as chief medical adviser to the Maharaja of Kapurthala (in the present-day state of Punjab) and as an army surgeon in the Russo–Japanese War. He was also a scholar, fluent in German, French, Italian, Sanskrit, Persian, Hindi, Punjabi and Arabic.

Mall's ongoing correspondence with the museum's curator C J S Thompson over the 11 years he spent in the Indian subcontinent raises questions about embracing diverse approaches to health, as well as about the intentions behind building and presenting a collection such as Wellcome's.

## Manuscripts and other objects bought in Srinagar.

Cap (Kashmiri) with several silver charms.

brass amilet necklace.

red Lingam.

very old stone Hindu medical deity.

Tibetan engraved (holy mantra) stone tablet.

Persian manuscript, Tenla and Magnan, with pictures (old)

Persian manuscript, animal logic.

jade engraved charms against several diseases.

Persian manuscript old.  (Medical).

Hanuman sketch.

forehead charms in silver, engraved with Koran verses.

I am asked by them to point out for your future guidance, when
similar plants come under your notice with some local reputation
that you should obtain:-

The native name.

The botanical name if possible, indicating the locality in which
the plant grows.

If it is obtainable in quantity, and if ample supplies could be
got with certainty.
What price it could be obtained for and transported to this
country.

## CODE FOR DR. MALL.

Manuscript  =  MS.

Price  =  figures  =  rupee

Object  =  OBJ.

Offer  =  OFFR.

Shall I buy?  =  SIB.

TELEGRAPH
Old Broad Street, Lond
Old Broad St., E.C. (Head Office:
8, Lime Street Square, E.C.
11, Mincing Lane, E.C.
an House, 6, Water Street.
y Chambers, corner of Clarence S
TATION in the United Kingdom.
19  at  9. 45
gar Kashm
ded } 26  1. 35
on

INDIA.

First published in 2017 by Wellcome Collection, part of the Wellcome Trust, 215 Euston Road, London NW1 2BE.

Published to accompany the Wellcome Collection exhibition *Ayurvedic Man*.

**wellcome collection**

www.wellcomecollection.org

Wellcome Collection is a free destination for the incurably curious.

It explores the links between medicine, life and art in the past, present and future. Wellcome Collection is part of the Wellcome Trust, a global charitable foundation dedicated to improving health. The Wellcome Trust is a charity registered in England and Wales, no. 210183.

*Ayurvedic Man* © The Wellcome Trust 2017

Introduction: Bárbara Rodríguez Muñoz
Design: Hato
Production: Petra Essing
Exhibition curator: Bárbara Rodríguez Muñoz
Curatorial adviser: Sita Reddy
Wellcome's collections researchers: Ruth Horry and Meghan Lambert

10 9 8 7 6 5 4 3 2 1

A CIP catalogue record for this book is available from the British Library.

ISBN 978-1-9998090-1-0

Printed and bound in Belgium by Cassochrome.

Every effort has been made to secure permission from all copyright holders. Any omissions and errors of attribution are unintentional and will, if notified in writing to the editor, care of the Wellcome Trust, be corrected in future printings.

The editors would like to thank all the contributors, lenders and supporters that have made this book possible, especially: artist Ranjit Kandalgaonkar; Robert Leckie and Joel Furness from Gasworks, London; Darshan Shankar from the TransDisciplinary University, Bengaluru; Sita Reddy and Professor Dominik Wujastyk; Mélanie Dautreppe-Liermann and Ken Kirton at Hato; and Bárbara Rodríguez Muñoz, Emily Sargent, Amy Higgitt, Marianne Templeton, Katherine Knowles, Luke Currall, Emma Smith, Chris Kingham, Ruth Horry, Meghan Lambert, Petra Essing, Fran Barrie, Kirty Topiwala, Zoe Middleton, Shelley Saggar, Rob Reddick, William Schupbach and Ross MacFarlane from Wellcome Collection.

All images courtesy of Wellcome Collection, London. Page 36—37, photograph by John Gribben

www.wellcomecollection.org/ayurvedicman